D1626500

Editor: Heather Dickson

Authors: Nick Daws *(Crash Landing, Hijack and Line of Destiny)*,
Christine Pountney *(Clockwork, Quarantine, A Close Call,
The Doctor's Daughter and A Glass of Sherry)*, Richard Skinner
(In the Land of the Pharaohs), Nick Hoare *(A Case of the Shakes and
Overdrive)*, Susan Everett *(The Ideal Man)*

Additional contributors: Lorna O'Connell, Russell Walton,
Rosie Atkins

Illustrator: Anni Jenkins

Page layout: Linley Clode

Cover design: Gary Inwood Studios

Published by: LAGOON BOOKS
PO BOX 311, KT2 5QW, UK

ISBN: 1899712291

Printed in France.

FIVE-MINUTE CLASSIC LATERAL THINKING PUZZLES

INTRODUCTION

This book contains 12 of the finest Lateral Thinking Puzzles ever invented - true classics of the genre that have perplexed and delighted people for generations. But here, with a new twist that is guaranteed to cause confusion, consternation, frustration and (ultimately) delight, these classic puzzles are buried in short stories that take no more than five minutes to read - but how long to solve?

...that depends on whether you work it out for yourself, or resort to deciphering the mirror writing solution provided after each story!

(The answer to each puzzle is in mirror writing - this will stop an accidental glance spoiling the fun. Just hold the page up to a mirror for the answer to be revealed.)

INDEX

A CASE OF
THE SHAKES

A CASE OF THE SHAKES

Dawson finally opened his eyes and peered through the cane blind. "Damn", he groaned. The sky was black. Huge angry clouds rolled over the plantation, swimming through the weak light that painted the morning in sickly shades of yellow.

If he were a religious man, he mused, he would be convinced that the end was nigh. This was the sort of thing that many of his workers believed, and accordingly, as well as the rains, this time of year always brought a noticeable drop in productivity. Back home, he would have put this down to sheer laziness, but after nearly twenty years in the province, he could see their point. Why, but ten days ago, when the rains had only just arrived, the entire village of San Pedro had been washed away after a downpour of just fifteen minutes' duration! Most of his workers had lost family or friends in the disaster, and now the general mood among them seemed to be that their village, San Alejandro de los Angeles, was next in line.

Many of his croppers sent their eldest sons up the valley, to the gorge just below the plantation, where they would construct makeshift shelters against the rain, and then spend all day and night watching the water levels. If the rain caused the levels to rise beyond the gorge's rocky sides, the boys were to send smoke signals and set off firecrackers, which would alert both the workers up at the plantation, and the women and old folk down in the village. That was the theory, anyhow. It hadn't helped San Pedro. The relentless rain had drenched the firewood and the firecrackers, and then a huge moving wall of rain water, river water and mud had claimed the lives of most of the San Pedro boys, before descending on the helpless village below.

None of this affected Dawson, though. The plantation was safely perched on top of a plateau, and his house was sturdily built on the highest part of it. Admittedly, this was the original site of the village, before his great-grandfather had claimed the land from the natives, but what was Dawson supposed to do? Feel guilty every day of his life? No one made the current villagers live where they did. They should learn to build better houses. This was, after all, the wettest part of what was famed to be a very wet country, with rainfall of more than twice the national average, and a rainy season of nearly five months' duration.

Five months! The thought turned something deep in Dawson's stomach. He hated the rains. He hated them with a passion. He hated them the way that some Europeans hated Winter. Five months of dank air, thunder, and mud. He couldn't think of anything worse.

He got out of bed and grudgingly dressed himself. When he was done, he glanced at his watch. Half-past nine. He knew he should be doing his rounds, checking on the croppers and the tally men, trying to keep productivity at something approaching a decent level. He resented doing this; it should be the tally men's work. The five months would pass slowly enough just watching the rain, without actually having to wander about in it - especially since he'd left his only raincoat and hat at his club the previous night.

9

Why risk getting soaked to the skin when he could stay in, have a drink, then get a lift with the Wallaces over to the club for a late lunch and cards? Immediately he remembered his doctor's grave tone at his last insurance medical. Then he remembered last week's incident with the Wallaces. He had tried to apologise the following day, but he couldn't really remember what he had said to their niece, and to cap it all, he'd slipped in a puddle on the way over to apologise, so as well as catching the rain he was so covered in mud it looked as if he'd spent all night in the gutter. Blow them all to hell, he thought. If he wanted to have a drink before work, who had the right to tell him otherwise?

After a concerted twenty-minute search of the entire house, he finally accepted that not only were all the bottles he could find entirely empty, but that all the ones he'd stashed away for just such an emergency, he'd already managed to find and finish. Damnation! He was now so angry that simply going off to work instead was out of the question. He wanted a drink, and nothing and nobody would stop him! He considered his options, which were few and far between. The nearest port of call was the Wallaces, but he somehow doubted that Wallace would be too sympathetic if it were seven on Saturday evening, let alone ten o'clock on a Monday morning. There was nothing for it. He would have to walk to the club.

Now this plan had many drawbacks, mainly that it was a good half-hour walk down through the plantation. Normally, the two-mile distance alone would have made him think twice, and now he didn't need to remind himself that he was slap-bang in the middle of the rainy season. He found himself cursing his own efficiency. The plantation was so well tended that, all the way from the house to the club, not a single plant of any sort grew over three and a half feet. This may have been the optimum cropping height for the local workers, but meant it would provide no shelter at all.

To add to his ire, he seemed to remember losing his old Royal and Ancient golfing umbrella to one of those young oafs working on the San Cristobal dam. Dashed bad cards, he thought. Probably all cheated. He started to look for another umbrella, then realised that his bottle search had covered all the possible hiding places. Damn.

His doctor had told him there was no point getting a car and learning to drive, partly because of his eyes but mainly because he was never halfway sober enough to drive. Damnation!

He could feel the fury rising. He simply had to have a drink...

By a quarter to eleven, Dawson was sitting in the deserted club bar, nursing a whisky sour, having demanded service from the manager. His anger had subsided, he felt at one with the world, and, most surprisingly of all, he was completely dry.

Dawson had walked the entire two miles to the club. Since he had no raincoat, no hat and no umbrella, how did he manage to get there without getting wet?

SOLUTION

It was the middle
of the rainy season
but, on the morning
Dawson walked
to the club, it
wasn't raining.

CLOCKWORK

CLOCKWORK

Saul Tabbot opened his eyes, looked at the clock on his bedside table and groaned. In eight minutes, it would be seven o'clock and time to get up. Saul resented being awake. Normally, he started his day promptly at seven o'clock after being awoken by the familiar sound of his alarm, but today he was out of synch. In Saul's mind, the fact that he'd woken up eight minutes too soon was a grave disruption to the strict routine of the entire day, which was regulated down to the smallest detail such as the temperature of the bath water or the time it took him to shave.

Saul crossed his arms under his head, listened to the sea outside and stared at a crack in the ceiling. That would have to be repaired, he thought to himself and remembered, as a child, watching his father plastering a crack in the ceiling. His father had stood stock-still on the ladder and applied the white paste with the precision of an artist. Saul could remember looking up through the steps and admiring his expertise. His father was good at everything and, perhaps driven by a need to compensate for the absence of Saul's mother who died during childbirth, demanded a great deal of Saul.

In the evenings, while the other children played outside, Saul had to sit at the kitchen table with a compass or a lead pencil, and chart weather systems on nautical maps, or memorise Shakespearean sonnets, while his father paced back and forth behind his chair with his hands clasped firmly behind his back. When Saul's father was convinced that he had imparted enough information to his son for one day, he would dismiss him to play with the other children. Saul would leave the house only to find that all the other children had been called inside to bed.

After a while, Saul gave up trying to be a normal boy. He gave up all his boyhood fantasies of becoming a racing-car driver, or a pilot, and dedicated himself to pleasing his father. He set himself the task of excelling even his father's perfectionism. He learned to be fastidious about timing, and acquired the habit of being meticulous about detail.

When his father died, Saul went to live on his own. He wanted to get as far away from his childhood as he possibly could. He had no friends and no living relatives that he knew of. He enjoyed the peace and quiet of his new-found solitude; above all, the freedom it gave him to pursue his passions.

In order to maintain the strict regimen of his daily routine, Saul hooked up all his lamps and electrical appliances to timers and energy-saving devices; every machine and light bulb in the house was connected to a system that turned them on automatically at various times during the day; all Saul had to do was turn them off.

Every evening at five-fifty, the radio would go on and Saul would sit down with a cup of tea for thirty-five minutes and listen to the shipping forecast, followed by the weather and the news; then he would get up, turn the radio off, go upstairs and switch on the only light in the house that he controlled manually.

Saul lay in bed and counted down the seconds before seven o'clock. He knew that as soon as his alarm went off, the coffee machine downstairs in the kitchen would start to percolate and that the hot water heater would kick in for his ritual eight o'clock bath. Every morning, like clockwork, Saul would get up, have his bath, and turn off the manual light.

That afternoon, at three-fifteen, Saul went down to the basement to get the ladder. He dragged it up the winding staircase to his bedroom and placed it directly under the crack in his ceiling. He prepared some filler and mounted the rickety steps to the top. He held his palette of white plaster in one hand, and a trowel in the other. He dragged a glob of the white stuff across the seam and then cleaned his trowel. Saul leaned out precariously to reach the far end of the crack and felt his foot slip. He rocked back and forth to get his balance but was unable to stabilise himself. The last thing Saul saw was the ceiling rushing away from him.

When Saul came to, it was raining. The wind had picked up and the house was creaking. He could hear the distant voice of the radio coming up through the floor-boards. Saul opened his eyes and looked up at the ceiling. He glanced around and saw that there were little flecks of filler all over the floor. Saul rolled over and sat up. He got to his feet and rubbed his eyes. It was dark outside and he felt dizzy. He raised a hand to his forehead and felt a large bump like half an orange.

Saul left his room and walked down the darkened hall. From the top of the stairs, he could clearly make out what the radio announcer was saying. He was introducing the ten o'clock news! Saul had been unconscious for nearly seven hours! The radio must have gone on at five-fifty and he hadn't been there to turn it off and go about the rest of his daily routine.

Saul gasped and raised a hand to cover his mouth. He turned and ran back to his bedroom. He rushed over to the window and pressed his face up against the cold glass. He just wanted to run - he pulled a suitcase out of his closet and started packing his clothes. He put on his rain boots and his waterproof coat. Just as he was opening the door to leave his house, a police cruiser pulled up and two policemen got out.

The following day this article appeared in the local paper:

Man Questioned in Connection with Death of Six People

Today, local authorities, in conjunction with the county police, are questioning Mr Saul Tabbot with regard to the untimely deaths, yesterday evening, of six people whose identities, for the sake of their families, have not yet been disclosed.

Why did Saul want to run, and why were the police so keen to question him regarding six deaths, when all he had done was fall off a ladder?

SOLUTION

Saul Talbot was a
lighthouse keeper. As he
was unconscious from
mid-afternoon until around
10pm, he had not turned on
the only light in the house
that he controlled manually
- the beacon light at the
top of the lighthouse
which guided sailors at sea.
By passing out, he had
inadvertently caused a
shipwreck in which six
sailors were killed.

CRASH LANDING

CRASH LANDING

The phone was ringing. Blearily, Marty opened his eyes. The digital clock by his bed told him it was 3:07am. This had better not be a wrong number, he thought.

He groped around the top of the bedside table and found the receiver on the third attempt.

"Marty Olsson," he said.

"Marty, get your butt down here now." It took Marty a few moments to recognise the voice of Michael Carver, managing director of Fivestar Airlines. Marty had never before heard him sound so rattled.

"What's happened?" he asked.

"A crash. One of our planes. Just get here, quick." The line went dead. Marty sat up in bed. For a second he stared at the receiver in his hand as though it had bitten him.

"Marty?" a small voice mumbled from the other side of his bed. 'S'matter?"

Marty cursed under his breath. Of all the nights for this to happen - the night he had finally lured the delectable Suzy Sheridan into his bed. "Sorry, babe, I've gotta go. It's an emergency."

Suzy raised herself on one elbow. She stared at him with big blue eyes through a lock of golden hair. "Oh, Marty. Do you have to?"

"'Fraid so." Marty had already hopped out of the bed and pulled on his suit pants. He headed for the bathroom.

'I'll call you. Help yourself to breakfast before you go."

As he drove across town, Marty switched on the radio. He was just in time to hear the announcer say: '...getting reports that a Fivestar Airlines' DC10 Airbus flying between New York and Chicago has crashed on the borders of Ohio, Indiana and Kentucky. At this stage it's not known if there are any survivors, and the airline has so far made no comment. More news as soon as we..."

Marty stabbed the 'off' button and the interior of the car was silent again. Driving one-handed, he lit a cigarette and drew deeply on it. Fivestar Airlines' wide-bodied DC10s could carry up to three hundred passengers. If the Airbus had been even half-full, that would make this one of the worst airline disasters in history. If the relatives sued, the company would probably go bust, leaving Marty just another unemployed PR signing on at the job agency. He put his foot hard down on the accelerator.

As he swung into the Fivestar lot, Marty noticed the red flashing lights of a trio of police cars. They were greatly outnumbered, however, by the Outside Broadcast units from NBC, ABC, CNN and a host of other national and local TV and radio stations. Marty parked as near the doors as he could. An ABC reporter recognised him: "Hey, Marty, is it true there are over two hundred dead?"

"No comment," Marty said, tight-lipped. He barged his way through the milling reporters and technicians and eventually made it to the foot of Fivestar Tower. Before the glass doors, a posse of grey-uniformed security men barred the way. Marty tried to push past them, but a big guy he hadn't seen before grabbed his arm.

21

"I told your buddy, now I'm telling you. No one gets in here without a pass. You understand?" The grip tightened.

"It's OK, Vince." With relief, Marty heard the familiar bass rumble of Con O'Hagan, Fivestar's security chief. "Marty's one of us. Let him through."

With ill grace, Vince released his grip and allowed Marty to pass. "Thanks, Con," Marty said, rubbing his arm where the guard's fingers had all but cut off the circulation. 'Where do I find MC?"

"Tenth floor. Boardroom."

Marty rushed across the foyer and into the express lift. Within half a minute he was walking into the large, oak-panelled boardroom of Fivestar Airlines. Michael Carver and the other directors were there. Carver's face was white, and he looked ten years older than the last time Marty had seen him. He was chain-smoking. His usual suave, imperturbable manner seemed to have deserted him completely.

"Marty. You've got to do something. Our plane's down, and there are nearly two hundred dead. The press are gonna crucify us."

Marty took a deep breath. "OK," he said.
'Tell me everything you know."

Once he'd got all the information and agreed a statement with the directors, Marty knew it was time to act. In the men's room he combed back his hair and adjusted his company tie. Then, moving slowly and deliberately, he made his way back to the foyer and out into the waiting throng. Microphones were instantly thrust in his face, and a moment later the TV arc lights were turned in his direction.

Questions rained in at him from every angle.

"What was...?"
"How many ... ?"
"Who did...?"
"Where are...?"

Marty raised both hands placatingly. "Come on, guys. You know the drill. I'll make a short statement, then try to answer any questions you may have. But first, let's get a bit more organised, shall we?" He paused as the reporters arranged themselves in a mêlée fractionally less chaotic. He held up a hand for silence, then glanced at his notes.

"I am authorised to read out the following statement which has been released by the directors of Fivestar Airlines. It says: 'At 02:17 hours, Eastern Standard Time, Sunday 23 November, a DC10 Airbus operated by Fivestar Airlines en route from Kennedy Airport, New York to O'Hare International Airport, in Chicago, crashed over Southwest Ohio. Fatalities were sustained. Emergency services were on the scene within twenty minutes, and a major accident investigation has already begun. The directors of Fivestar Airlines deeply regret the loss of life and the anguish caused to the families of those concerned. All other DC10s in the Fivestar fleet have been grounded, and the airline will take every possible step to find out the cause of this terrible accident." Marty looked up. Immediately the barrage of questions resumed.

"One at a time," Marty begged, raising his voice to make himself heard. From the corner of his eye he saw Ted Taylor, the veteran NBC reporter. "Ted?"

"Where exactly did the Fivestar plane come down, Mr Olsson?"

"In farmland near Cincinnati, Ohio."

"And how many fatalities were there?"

Marty glanced at his notes, though in fact the figures were seared in his brain. "The latest figures I have are a hundred and ninety-two dead, and another twelve injured."

From somewhere at the back of the media ruck there came a low whistle. A young woman in a yellow duffel coat pushed forward: "Jill Farmer, WAGH, Chicago. Mr Olsson, is there any truth in the rumour that a bomb threat was received at the airline minutes before the plane took off?"

"We have no record of any such threat," Marty said smoothly, though inside he was shaken. In fact, Carver told him a threat had been received, but in an airline office such threats were a routine matter. There had been no reason to take it any more seriously than any of the other crank calls the airline received every week. In any event, no record had been made, so his reply to Jill Farmer's question was strictly accurate. He hoped she had simply been fishing for a story rather than following a genuine lead.

"So what caused the plane to crash?" a CNN reporter asked. "Was it pilot error?"

"It's much too early to say," Marty said, relieved to be fielding an easier question. "Our team of investigators has already gone to the site to try to recover the flight recorder box which should provide all the answers we need. Until we've had their report, there is really no point in speculation."

"But your statement said that all other DC10s in the fleet

have been grounded," the CNN man said. "Does that mean the airline suspects mechanical failure?"

Marty grinned inwardly. "It's just a routine precaution," he said, the familiar line tripping from his tongue with practised ease. "At this stage we have no reason to suspect mechanical problems, but at Fivestar Airlines the safety of our customers is, of course, our very highest priority."

Jill Farmer caught his eye again. He hoped this question would be less disconcerting than the last one she had posed.

"Mr Olsson, I understand the plane crashed almost exactly on the borders of Ohio, Indiana and Kentucky. In which of those states' morgues will the bodies of the survivors be held until they are identified and transported home? Or is New York State taking charge of this as the flight's originating state, or Illinois, since Chicago was the destination?"

"I, uh..." Marty stared at his notes again. "I can't answer that, Ms Farmer. Does anyone else have any..?"

But another reporter took up the question. "Yes, which morgue, Mr Olsson?"

Marty tried to smile, but had a feeling it was coming out lopsided. "Thanks, ladies and gentlemen. I'll, uh, get back to you as soon as I have more news." He turned on his heel and hastened back to Fivestar Tower.

American law varies from state to state, especially as regards the basics such as birth, marriage and death, and Marty was clearly unable to answer the question posed. Can you figure out which morgue would be most likely to hold the bodies?

SOLUTION

It doesn't matter where the plane crashed, the survivors would not be placed in a morgue.

QUARANTINE

QUARANTINE

Brent Wood was trimming the claws on his favourite animal in the zoo, the snow leopard, when his director called him over and told him the bad news. Brent hung his hands through the wire fence and listened to the director tell him about the rising deficit, the decline in donations and drastic but unavoidable budget cuts. The director shrugged his shoulders and told Brent that his snow leopard was one of three big cats in the zoo that were being traded for animals with a lower maintenance cost. Brent had two days to prepare his animal for transportation; the snow leopard was heading north.

Before getting the job at the Wildlife Zoo, Brent had spent two years in the mountains of Central Asia tracking the rare and beautiful *panthera uncia* and studying its nocturnal habits. He didn't like the idea of keeping wild animals in cages but, after a while, he decided that the snow leopards in captivity needed his help more than the ones that were free. For the previous ten months, Brent had been canvassing to raise money for an organisation in Mongolia where abandoned cubs were cared for and later returned to their natural habitat. His dream was, one day, to see the snow leopard taken off the endangered species list.

Brent was the only person who was allowed in the snow leopard's den. He knew how to handle the big cat by rubbing the soft fur between her eyes in a circular motion. The snow leopard trusted him and would take food directly from his hand, but if anybody else impinged on her territory, she would bare her teeth and paw the ground with her blunted claws.

The situation in the tiger's den was similar. The only person the tiger would allow inside his cage was Emily Shackle, a small, thin-boned woman who had nursed the tiger when it first arrived at the zoo. Emily was a trained vet and had worked for eight years in a basement surgery in South London. One day she grew tired of working with domestic cats and dogs and left her practice in search of wilder animals. She got as far as the Wildlife Zoo, arriving the same day as the then five-month-old Bengal tiger cub. The official trainer had put his back out and was away on sick leave. To Emily's delight, the zoo director was in desperate need of a qualified volunteer and Emily got her first assignment. After she had proved herself with the tiger, Emily became a full-time member of staff and the only keeper to gain the tiger's confidence.

The zoo had one other impressive cat, the black panther. She was notoriously unpredictable and mistrustful of people. She had been mistreated by her former owners, who belonged to a travelling Romanian circus troupe, and when she got to the zoo, her fur was matted and she had deep lacerations where her collar had been. She'd been teased and prodded all her life so that, as soon as she got a whiff of a human being, her lips would curl back to reveal sharp incisors. The panther was fully grown and her body length measured over six feet.

The only person in the zoo who dared approach her was Edmund Black.

Edmund was something of a wild card himself, and had a temper to match the panther's. He'd been in foster care all his life, moving from one family to the next, until he was old enough to move out on his own. When he first set eyes on the panther and saw the quick darting eyes and the bristling hair, he immediately felt that he'd found a kindred spirit. Those who saw him working with the animal said that he had an uncanny way with her; that it was almost as if there was a telepathic bond between the two.

The director went from the snow leopard's den, where he'd spoken to Brent, to tell Emily that she too needed to prepare her animal for transportation. He found her brushing down the tiger's tawny coat while it lay licking its chops and playing with a clean, white bone - all that remained of twelve pounds of raw meat. When she heard the news, she kneeled down and hugged the tiger.

The tiger put a leathery paw on her back and nudged the top of her head with its bloody muzzle.

The director stood watching Emily interact with the tiger, then turned slowly on his heels and went to speak with Edmund. The director was afraid of his reaction; the panther meant everything to him. Since Edmund had been working with the cat, he had become more gentle-mannered and smiled more often. However, the director could still remember the terrible tantrums Edmund used to throw and was somewhat nervous as he approached the panther pen. When he got there, he was glad to see Edmund inside the fenced-off area and was sheepishly relieved to be speaking to him through the wire barrier. When Edmund heard the news that he would be parting company with the majestic panther, he grabbed the fence and rattled it for all he was worth. The director stumbled backwards.

The very next morning, Edmund appeared in the doorway of the director's office. He looked calm and was holding his cap in his hands. He apologised profusely for his behaviour the day before and requested to be involved, with the other two keepers, in the transportation process. Since Edmund was the only trainer who could handle the black panther, the director had to acquiesce.

"However, there are a few things I need to tell you about the arrangements," the director said. "I want you to listen very carefully and relay every detail to Brent and Emily."

"Yes, sir," Edmund said and sat down across from the director who slid him a piece of paper and a pen.

"You'll need to take notes," said the director. "This is of the utmost importance."

"Yes, sir."

"First of all, as you know, money is tight. The budget will only allow for the rental of a small truck and driver. Besides the driver, there is only room enough for two passengers at a time, that is, two people at a time, or two animals at a time, or an animal and a person."

"We'll work it out amongst ourselves, sir," Edmund said.

"Yes, but there's one more thing," the director continued. "I have my suspicions about this driver. I would have much rather gone with a reputable company, but with only £1,200 to spend..."

"I understand," Edmund said.

"I am afraid," the director said, lowering his voice, "that if he doesn't have something or someone to deliver at the other end, he might just take off with the money. So this is what I am trusting you to tell Brent and Emily: the truck must never travel empty and I've negotiated with the driver, and I have it in writing, that he will make a maximum of nine journeys back and forth if necessary, but no more. Have you got all that, Edmund?"

"Yes, sir."

"First thing tomorrow morning, you, Brent and Emily will take the cats and stay with them in the zoo's holding pen. The animals will remain in quarantine for twenty-four hours while they receive a thorough check by our vets - for disease, infection, routine stuff. When the cats arrive up north, they will again be put in quarantine for twenty-four hours while the vets from the Paradise Zoo make sure that the animals are in excellent condition."

"The panther is perfect," Edmund said.

"I'm sure she is. It's just a formality. Now, do you have any questions, Edmund?"

"Let me just get this straight. We've got nine trips in which to transport the three cats from the holding pen in the south to the holding pen in the north. However, only a maximum of two passengers can go at any given time, and by passengers I mean, either animals or trainers or both. What's more, the truck can never travel empty."

'You've got it."

"Right," Edmund said. "And the animals will be held in quarantine at either end, in the same pen along with their trainers."

"Yes."

"But there is something you don't seem to understand, director. These animals are the most volatile animals in the zoo, the most dangerous animals to be around. I can't leave Brent or Emily with the panther; Brent can't leave Emily or myself with the snow leopard; and Emily, in turn, knows how dangerous it would be if she left Brent or myself with the Bengal tiger."

"So what you're saying," said the director, "is that no animal can be left alone at either end with another trainer unless that other trainer's animal is also present."

"Exactly!" Edmund shouted. "How are we going to do this?"

"Well, how the hell should I know? What do I pay you for? Work it out amongst yourselves. Now get out of my office."

Edmund looked at the director for a moment and pondered whether or not he should let the director get away with such a shameless eschewal of responsibility.

Edmund was about to protest when he thought about the sleek panther pacing its cage, and his mind became suddenly focused on doing the most he could to ensure that she had a safe journey up north. If the Paradise Zoo could afford her, then maybe they had better facilities too. They might even pay him to continue looking after the cat. He was, after all, the only person the panther trusted.

Edmund stood up slowly and donned his cap. He thrust his hands deep inside his trouser pockets. "We're going to do this," he said to the director. "We're going to get those cats up north, but it won't be thanks to you."

Edmund, Brent and Emily did manage to get themselves and their animals to the Paradise Zoo in nine journeys. How?

SOLUTION

Edmund, Brent and Emily would have had to arrange their journeys as follows:

On Journey 1, Edmund Black and the panther go north. On Journey 2, Edmund Black goes south. On Journey 3, the snow leopard and tiger go north. On Journey 4, the snow leopard goes back south again. On Journey 5, Brent Wood takes the snow leopard north again. On Journey 6, Brent Wood goes south again. On Journey 7, Brent Wood and Emily Shackle go north. On Journey 8, Emily Shackle goes south again. On Journey 9, Emily Shackle and Edmund Black join the others in the north.

A CLOSE CALL

A CLOSE CALL

Ray Bones stretched and looked at his wristwatch. He'd done two hours of overtime on top of his eight hour shift and it was now five to ten. He threw his newspaper into the wastepaper basket, stood up and pushed his chair in, locked the office and left the building. Ray walked the whole length of Coldharbour Lane, from Brixton to Camberwell, and by the time he got to Camberwell Green, it was nearly eleven o'clock. He was hot and thirsty. He walked into his local pub, the Hermit's Cave, and took his usual seat at the bar. Billy pulled a pint of Winter Warmer while Ray lit a cigarette.

"Here you go, Bones" Billy said.

"Cheers, mate," Ray said, raising his glass at Billy then downing half the pint in one swallow. "Ahh."

"Sometimes I wish we weren't friends," Billy said.

"Why's that?"

"'Cause you're a bartender's worst nightmare."

"Aw, come on," Ray said. "I'm your best customer. I drink half my wages in here every week."

"Sure, but with the amount of damage you've done, it's a wonder I break even."

"Go easy on me, Billy. I can't help it."

"Sure. But I'm warning you, Ray. I'm going to cut you off when I think you've had your limit."

"Who do you think you are?" Ray asked. "My mother?"

"No, but let me tell you, I've been tempted to call her sometimes and get her to take you home."

"Leave my mother out of this," Ray said. "And get me another pint, will you?"

Billy poured Ray another and took his money and went over to the cash register and brought back the change.

Ray took his wallet out of his pocket and counted his money. He had twelve pounds left. He did a quick calculation. He could drink four more pints and still afford the cab fare home. If he really needed a fifth, he could always walk or, better yet, maybe one of his mates would show up and buy a round. Ray looked at his watch again.
It was eleven-thirty.

At eleven thirty-five, Berry Klein kissed his wife and headed out to the car. He unlocked the door and got inside. He clipped his cab identification card to the sun visor and started the car. It was a brand new Toyota Corolla and he liked to warm up the engine before pulling out. He sat for a while with his hands in his lap, then he wiped the windscreen with the sleeve of his shirt. He looked up at the mug shot on his ID card. His wife didn't like the way he looked so serious - almost menacing, she had said, but Berry thought it looked professional; the way it should be. He took his job very seriously. He figured that people were putting their lives in his hands, and he had to respect that.

After a few minutes, Berry pulled out into the street, switched on the two-way radio, and checked in with Cassandra at the main office.

"There's a pick-up at Buckingham Palace," she said and laughed across the shortwaves. "Just joking, Berry. How are you, luv?"

"It's a fine day, Cassandra," Berry said smiling to himself. One of the joys of his job was working with Cassandra. She always made him laugh. She was the only person in the world who could crack that serious expression on his face.

"Pick up in Kensington" she would say and Berry would melt like butter, but as soon as he had a customer in his cab, he would switch off the radio and revert to his natural seriousness. Berry's greatest fear was having an accident.

Three years ago, when Berry had started driving a cab, he had witnessed a fatal crash. A young woman had driven off the road and into a lamp-post. Berry had stopped the car and run over to help. The woman had died on impact but there was a baby in the back seat. Berry had held the screaming child until the ambulance arrived. For months afterwards, the sound of that baby crying had plagued him. He would have nightmares and wake screaming in the middle of the night. His wife had urged him to give up the job and he almost did until, one day, he realised that what people needed more than anything else was safe transportation. So Berry devoted himself to being the best driver he could be. He boasted about the fact that he had many repeat customers, especially women, who felt safe in his company.

At one-thirty, Ray stumbled out of the Hermit's Cave, blind drunk. He had finished off four more pints at the bar and was about to leave, with enough money still left in his pocket to take a cab home, when he decided to have

40

another, and walk the two miles to Peckham where he lived in a rundown tower block. Outside, he could barely see a thing because his eyelids kept slipping down over his eyeballs. He kept a hand on the buildings to steady himself and started off in the direction of home.

It was a miracle that Ray survived because every time he crossed an intersection he didn't stop for traffic, but continued to lunge down the street like a lunatic. His habit of dressing entirely in black, as indeed he was dressed today, did little to help matters.

Just after Ray had crossed Peckham High Street, he walked up a long, damp, completely unlit alley that ran between a row of tall buildings. It just so happened that Berry was at the same time driving down the same alley, having dropped off a young woman at the back door of a hair salon, where she worked. Ray stopped in his tracks and watched as Berry's car sped towards him - with no headlights on. He stood frozen - paralysed by the fear of his own imminent death.

Sitting in his cab, Berry saw his life flash before him. He had been listening to Cassandra's voice over the radio and was momentarily distracted. At the very last moment he was able to brake hard, and stopped less than a metre short of Ray, but not before making a promise to himself to hand over his licence and give up driving altogether.

Since Berry's headlights were not on, and Ray was dressed entirely in black, how was Berry able to see Ray in the unlit alley in time to avoid hitting him?

SOLUTION

Berry could see Ray
since it was daylight and
there was no need for his
car lights to be on. Ray
was a night-watchman
and he left work at 10am
(not 10pm). When he left
the pub, it was 1.30pm
(not 1.30am).

THE DOCTOR'S DAUGHTER

THE DOCTOR'S DAUGHTER

The sun hovered like a fiery ball over the frozen flatlands of the Russian steppes. Jacques Gallante reined in his horse and surveyed the battlefield. His troops had fought bravely but lost and now, everywhere he looked, he saw the slow, twisting bodies of gravely wounded men. These were his men, under his charge, and they had always looked to him for leadership; however, for the first time during his two years in the campaign, he felt that he had failed as an officer. Up to now he had served Napoleon with unfailing loyalty, but as he looked out at his massacred battalion, he questioned the legitimacy of the wars. He felt powerless to stop the deluge of blood that seeped out across the snow and ice. The field that just last night had lain undisturbed and pristine in the twilight was now a sea of red.

Jacques pulled a small telescope out from under his heavy greatcoat and held it up to his right eye. The brass ring of the eyepiece was still warm. Far off in the distance, he located a band of Cossacks riding swiftly towards the east in their thick fur coats and hats. He knew that his army was not equipped to fight these men who were accustomed to the bitterly cold climate. Jacques stood up in his stirrups and swivelled round to look in the direction they were heading. In the growing dark of the evening, he could just make out the faint orange glow and dark grey smoke of the burning city of Moscow. He realised then that the situation was catastrophic. Napoleon and his army would have to retreat.

As Jacques was sitting astride his horse, a young soldier stumbled over and grabbed hold of his boot. He had lost his uniform and stood shivering in a threadbare shirt. His chest and back were soaked with blood.

"The doctor," he said. "Get the doctor and bring him back. It's our only hope...the boy..." he continued, "he's in agony. I promised his mother I would look after him. He's not yet fifteen years old. You have to help me."

Jacques looked down at the young soldier. "What's your name?" he asked.

"Frederick Gaston."

"God be with you, Frederick," he said and withdrew a flask of brandy from his pocket and handed it to the soldier. Then he swung his horse round, dug his spurs into its muscular flanks and galloped off.

Night had fallen and it was pitch black and devilishly cold when Jacques arrived back in the village. He drew up and dismounted outside the cottage that had been requisitioned by the doctor to serve as the infirmary. He looped the reins over a fence and headed for the door. Throughout the campaign, the army had always granted the doctor's requests for comfortable accommodation because he was accompanied by his daughter, an attractive young lady, who was working as a nurse. However, some people resented the doctor and said he took advantage of this preferential treatment. Jacques had always defended the doctor against such accusations, arguing that he performed an invaluable service; so he didn't think to knock but barged straight into the house calling for the doctor.

The cottage was stuffy and hot and a roaring fire blazed in the hearth. The table in the centre of the room was strewn with the remains of a decadent meal of roasted meat and black bread; there were two empty bottles of army-issue officers' vodka. In the corner of the room, on a low wooden bench, the doctor lay sleeping. His mouth was open and he was snoring loudly. Jacques went over and shook him violently. The doctor stirred and mumbled something but did not wake. Jacques shook him again and the doctor rolled off the bench and onto the floor; but still he did not wake. Jacques was livid with indignation. He thought of his men dying on the battlefield, freezing to death and starving. He ran his fingers through his hair and once again surveyed the room.

Beside the hearth was a door leading to another room. Jacques strode briskly towards the door and peered inside. On the far wall, above a bed, a single candle burned under an icon of Saint Christopher. There was a large lump in the bed and Jacques walked across and stood over it and heard the heavy breathing of not one, but two sleepers. With mounting anger, he took hold of the corner of the feather bedspread and flung it back. The doctor's daughter lay curled up naked except for a flimsy petticoat. Lying beside her was one of his fellow officers, a young nobleman by the name of Francois Chateau.

"This is an outrage!" he yelled, pulling the young lady out of bed and placing his hands around Francois' neck. "You are a disgrace and a deserter!" he yelled, shaking him furiously. "You have let your men down! How dare you! Get out of bed, you useless drunk!"

Francois opened his eyes and his hands shot up to pry the fingers loose from around his neck. The doctor's daughter ran out of the room screaming for her father. Jacques pressed his full weight down onto the other man's neck, pinning him to the bed. Francois could not breathe. He rolled over and managed to get up into a kneeling position, then punched Jacques in the stomach hard enough to wind him. Jacques staggered backwards, gasping for breath. He put his hand out and leaned against the wall. Without taking his eyes off Jacques, Francois swung his feet down onto the floor, sat up on the edge of the bed, and started to get dressed.

"Listen..." he began to say, but Jacques raised his hand as if to halt someone in the road and began, finger by finger, to remove the leather glove of his left hand. When he had slipped it off, he raised it in the air and threw it to the floor.

"You are not worthy to be an officer," he said. "However, I am glad that we share the same title and rank, if only for the reason that I may now challenge you to a duel."

Jacques then turned on his heels and left the room, ignoring Francois' undignified and pathetic pleas to retract the challenge. Jacques shoved to one side the young lady who was crying on her father's breast, picked the doctor up by the scruff of his neck, and carried him over his shoulder and out of the house. He slung the doctor over the horse, mounted up behind him and galloped back to the battlefield.

That night Francois was visited by Jacques' seconds. They met with Francois' seconds and negotiated the terms of the duel. It was to take place the next morning, one hour after sunrise, two miles west of the village. The duel was to be fought with pistols at a distance of ten paces apiece from the designated spot. Both men would have two pistols containing one bullet each. The duel would be fought to the death. Both men agreed to forfeit the requirement that the doctor be present, as he was still in the field tending to the wounded men.

Jacques woke after a brief and fitful sleep, saddled his horse and, accompanied by his two seconds, rode out into the black and frosty morning. The sky was clear and a blue moon still shimmered on the icy steppes. Jacques watched his hot breath rise in the cold air and thought how precious it was and that it might be his last.

When he arrived at the appointed site, Francois was already there. The seconds conferred and approved the shiny black pistols chosen for the duel. Jacques removed his greatcoat and gave it to one of his seconds saying that, if he should die, his coat was to be given to a young soldier by the name of Frederick Gaston. He then took his two pistols and walked towards Francois who was waiting for him. The two men met and bowed to each other, then both walked ten paces in opposite directions; Francois facing west and Jacques facing east towards the ever-brightening sky. Jacques wondered if he would ever see such a sun rise again and he grew sad and melancholic. He suddenly felt very tired, and finally saw the pointlessness of war and all its destruction.

Out of the corner of his eye, he saw his second raise a white handkerchief in the air. This was the signal for the officers to prepare themselves. When the handkerchief dropped, the duel would begin.

The second shouted "Ready?", then dropped the handkerchief. Four shots rang out. Neither Jacques nor Francois turned around but it was all over in the blink of an eye. Both men lay on the ground, dead from bullet wounds to the heart and chest.

As neither man turned around, how did they fatally shoot each other?

SOLUTION

After meeting and bowing, the two men had taken ten paces backwards, not forwards. Hence, when the handkerchief was dropped, signalling the start of the duel, they were facing each other (one facing east, the other west) and were therefore able to see, and shoot, each other.

THE IDEAL MAN

THE IDEAL MAN

Theresa strutted up the street, passing a man resembling Frankenstein who was carrying a six-pack of lager. She presumed they were heading for the same place. The dull thud of distant music led them both towards the same house. Sally opened the door, still sober enough to remember to greet her guests. She smiled at her best friend.

"Theresa! Great! Now we can have some fun."

Theresa was impressed with Sally's outfit - fake black and white Dalmatian fur and matching wig for a wicked Cruella De Vil. She wished that she'd made more of an effort with her costume.

"Who are you then?" Sally scrutinised the brown dress underneath Theresa's coat. "Give me a clue."

Frankenstein squeezed past them, groaning.

Theresa frowned.

"It's not my fault that I can't guess it." Sally led her friend inside.

Theresa frowned again. Sally was confused.

"The Mona Lisa!" Theresa gushed. "You know, with that glum face."

"But it's more of a smirk," Sally pouted. "And anyway, the Mona Lisa never wore skirts as short as that."

"OK, OK," the young woman conceded. "I should have worn a better costume. But I don't know, Sal, you throw a party and give me a chance to meet some blokes and I can't tell what they really look like. They're all aliens and cowboys."

"That Frankenstein seemed to like you."

"Get lost. He's not my type."

Sally led her friend past some milkmaids to the kitchen, and pulled a bottle of white wine out of the fridge.

"Before you start moaning on about how you never meet the right man, there's something you should know," whispered Sally, spotting a policeman in the hallway. "You can't say I never do anything for you...there are four bachelors here tonight."

"Bachelors. That's such a funny word."

"Single then." Sally poured them both a drink. "Available."

Theresa wasn't overly optimistic. "But Sal, you know the only type of man I'd go for is one who's tall, rich and has big brown eyes."

"You forgot handsome," Sally grinned.

"That goes without saying."

Sally led Theresa by the hand towards the living room and the deep pulsating music. "Follow me," she trilled. "Sadly only one of the four guys is rich and only two have big brown eyes, but each of them meets at least one of your requirements and one is perfect: tall and rich with big brown eyes. You won't be disappointed."

"Great party, Sally!" Captain Kirk gave a cheery wave.

"Him?" Theresa immediately perked up. This was looking interesting. She realised her guess was wrong when Princess Leia appeared and gave the man a kiss. Plenty more fish in the sea. Four of them at least...

"Come and try the dip," smiled Sally. "There's salsa." Sally was making strange twitching movements with her head. Theresa realised this was some kind of sign, and scuttled to her side.

"There," Sally pointed at the far corner. "Single man number one, Michael." Then over at the drinks table. "Paul and Simon..." Sally nodded at a man chatting with some friends. "And last but not least, Jonathon."

Theresa smiled. "Not bad going, Sally! I can see that three of them are tall and two have big brown eyes. I'd call this a most impressive start."

"Of course. We aim to please."

"So who's who? Which one's got all three?" Theresa glanced across at the four men.

Sally smiled, teasing. "That's for me to know and you to find out." Grinning, she wandered off to chat to some other guests, glancing back to see who Theresa aimed for first.

"Psst!" Theresa caught her friend's attention. "You could at least introduce me."

"Hello. Are you a friend of Sally's?"

Theresa spun around and saw Michael behind her, drink in hand. She smiled. Not a bad start to the evening.

"Yes, and you?"

"Yes, from work. My name's Michael."

"I know. Sally told me."

"Right." Michael supped his beer, froth clinging to his upper lip. "And you are?"

Theresa did her frown. Michael didn't understand. Theresa tried a lighter smirk.

"Think art. Think Italy. Think Leonardo da Vinci."

Michael looked her up and down, still vague.

"The Mona Lisa!" she exclaimed.

"Oh, right." The man was obviously not impressed. 'I meant, what's your name?"

Theresa told him, and watched him wander off. What was so original about his outfit, anyway?

She turned around to find Paul at her side. "I'm Theresa, and before you ask, I've come as the Mona Lisa, not as myself or my look-alike cousin Val."

"I'm Paul," the young man smiled. "And I'm supposed to be..."

Theresa nodded, having drained her glass. "I can tell. Very nice."

Paul dutifully headed for the drinks table and brought back a bottle of wine, quickly refilling Theresa's glass. She was starting to enjoy herself. This was rather fun. Both he and Michael had the same coloured eyes.

"I'll be back in a minute," Theresa raised her voice over the music, shouting up into Paul's ear. "Don't go away."

She rushed off to the toilet, but it was occupied. Theresa leant against the wall. Four single men. Three tall, two with brown eyes and only one who was rich. It was like that Christmas song. Two turtle doves, three French hens...something like that. She'd soon work it out.

The toilet flushed and Cat Woman came out. One of her stockings had laddered. Theresa didn't know whether to mention it or not.

When she got downstairs, Theresa found Paul standing with Simon, having a man talk about football. She smiled. They were quite different in appearance, but, as they were standing next to each other, she could see they were both exactly the same height. This was getting interesting.

"Look, it's the Mona Lisa!" Simon grinned. Theresa was impressed. Intelligence as well. "Paul told me," the man

56

admitted. "That's a lovely dress."

"Thanks." Theresa's eyes flitted between Paul and Simon, enjoying the flirtation. She looked around for Sally, but her friend was nowhere to be seen. She smiled across at Jonathon, who gave a little wave. She noticed that he and Simon were not of the same stature.

"Hi. I'm Theresa." She shook hands with the last man. "I've heard a lot about you."

"Really?" Jonathon seemed surprised.

"I like your outfit. Very smart."

Theresa was having fun. She had to go and tell Sally. She found her friend in the kitchen, refilling the punch bowl.

"He's a bit like Tom Cruise in 'Top Gun'," Theresa gushed. "He's perfect!"

"Only he's not tall," Sally frowned.

"Who?"

"Tom Cruise. He's only five feet something."

"Well, then he takes second place," Theresa smiled, "because I've already found my number one."

Theresa headed back to the party, drink in hand. She smiled. She'd found her ideal man.

Who was Theresa's ideal man? Who was tall and rich with big brown eyes?

SOLUTION

We know that Simon and Jonathon are not the same height, yet Simon is the same height as Paul and if a total of three men are tall, then we can deduce that Michael, Paul and Simon are tall and Jonathon is short.

As only one man is rich, he must be the ideal man and therefore Jonathon, who is short, cannot be rich. As every man must have at least one attribute, Jonathon must therefore have brown eyes.

We know that Michael and Paul have the same colour of eyes, so we can assume, since only two men have big brown eyes, that neither Michael or Paul have (because Jonathon definitely has). Therefore Simon must have big brown eyes - and he, therefore, is also the man who is rich.

Theresa's ideal man is Simon.

IN THE LAND OF THE PHARAOHS

IN THE LAND OF THE PHARAOHS

In the Land of Canaan, a wealthy man had twelve sons by four women. Ten of his sons were shepherds, looking after the sheep that their father owned, but the two youngest sons were not yet old enough to help their brothers. The father's favourite son was the second youngest. When the favourite was seventeen, his father made a beautiful, multi-coloured robe for him, which had long sleeves and stretched down to the ground. The other brothers were very jealous.

After being given the robe, the favourite son started to have vivid dreams. One morning, he told his brothers he had dreamt they were making wheat sheaves in the fields. His sheaf stood upright, but his brothers' sheaves were badly made. In his dream, all the sheaves made by them came and bowed down to his. A few mornings later, the favourite son told them about another dream he'd had. He said that the sun, moon and eleven stars all bowed down before him. The brothers were angry. "Do you think you will one day rule over us?" they asked him.

Soon afterwards, the wealthy father deemed his favourite son old enough to help his brothers tend the sheep and sent him out into the fields. The son walked into the countryside looking for his brothers, but couldn't find them. He met a stranger and asked him if he had seen his brothers. The stranger said that he had seen them walking towards a village called Dothan. The favourite son thanked him and set off for the village.

The brothers were sitting by a well, with the sheep nearby, when they saw their brother approach Dothan.
They imagined their father had sent him to take control.
They hated him so much that they talked about killing him. One of the brothers, Reuben, grew alarmed and pleaded with the others to spare the boy's life. He pointed to the well and suggested leaving him there. The brothers agreed.

When the favourite son came up to them, the brothers grabbed him, tore off his beautiful robe and threw him down the well. They ripped the robe to pieces and covered it with goat's blood. When they arrived home, they told their father they had found the robe lying on the ground. The father broke down with grief - believing his favourite son to have been devoured by a wild animal.

A caravan of Midianite merchants were passing through Dothan and discovered the favourite son at the bottom of the well. They took him out and carried him with them. They crossed the Nile into Egypt and entered the town of Goshen, where they traded their gum tragacanth, raisins, myrrh and balm. The merchants then sold the son for twenty pieces of silver to Potiphar, who was one of the Pharaoh's eunuchs.

Potiphar soon realised that the favourite son was quick-witted and trustworthy and so put him in charge of his house and property. One of Potiphar's wives was greatly taken with the son and, when Potiphar was away one day, she asked him to lie with her. He refused, saying he couldn't betray the trust shown in him by Potiphar.

She asked him again and, when he refused once more, she grabbed him, but the son ran out of the house, tearing his robe in the process. The wife ran out into the street after him, shouting that he had tried to rape her. The son was quickly caught and imprisoned.

In jail, the son made a name for himself as an interpreter of dreams. All the prisoners came to him and told them their dreams, and he would advise them of their meanings. The son was correct every time and soon word got around that he had great powers of prophecy. Even the Pharaoh heard about the son's powers and demanded to see them demonstrated firsthand. The favourite son was brought before the Pharaoh and made to listen to him recount a strange dream about seven fat cows and seven lean cows. The son said that the next seven years would be a time of abundance for Egypt, but that the seven years afterwards would see a famine spread through the land.

The Pharaoh looked at the son and admired the courage of his words. He decided to have faith in him and ordered his release. He put the son in charge of his house. That year, the harvest was plentiful, but the Pharaoh instructed that a part of it should be put aside and saved. The year after saw another good harvest and the Pharaoh gave the same instructions. This happened for several years, during which time he became more and more fond of the son, believing him to be of sound judgement. After seven years, the harvest failed and a terrible famine struck the whole of Egypt and Canaan. The Pharaoh, however, was able to provide for his people and he made the son governor of all Egypt.

In Canaan, the famine had dreadful consequences. The wealthy father sent all but his youngest son, Benjamin, to Egypt, where he'd heard there was food to buy. When they arrived at the Pharaoh's house, they were met by their brother. Although they no longer recognised him, he recognised them and was very moved when he saw them. When they explained what they'd come for, the favourite son accused them of being spies. He said they had really come to assess the defences of the town before they attacked. The brothers protested wildly and showed him the pieces of silver they had brought. "Why would we bring silver if we intended to attack you?" they said. He told them that one of their number would be imprisoned while the others should return to Canaan and come back with their youngest brother.

The brothers talked among themselves in their own language about what to do. Reuben chided them and made them see that they were being punished for the killing of their brother. They didn't realise that their brother could understand everything they said. He went into another room and wept. The brothers chose Simeon to stay behind and, when the others left for Canaan, Simeon was imprisoned.

They explained to their father what had happened in Egypt and what the governor demanded. The father was full of concern. He had lost one son and was sure he would never see his youngest again if he assented to the governor's wishes. He made his sons vow not to return home without Benjamin and, when they had promised, he finally agreed. Although his family was starving, the wealthy man sent pistachio nuts, almonds, spices, honey, balm and myrrh as well as double the amount of silver in order to appease the governor.

The brothers returned to Egypt. When they were with the governor again, they presented Benjamin to him. The favourite son looked at Benjamin for a moment, then instructed a steward to slaughter a fatted calf and prepare a lavish meal for the brothers. He ordered Simeon's release and then left them. On his own, he cried after seeing his only natural brother again.

While the brothers were eating their meal, the favourite son instructed a steward to give the brothers all the grain they could carry. In the top of each bag of grain, he told the steward to put the silver they had given for the food. He also instructed the steward to plant a silver cup in one of the bags. It should be ensured that Benjamin would carry this bag, he said. The steward did what the governor instructed.

In the morning, all eleven brothers thanked the governor and left for Canaan. After only a few miles, the steward and some of his men caught up and stopped them. He told them that one of the governor's silver cups was missing and he had orders to search their bags and imprison anyone found with the cup. The brothers protested their innocence, saying they had always come in peace and with honest intentions, but the steward brushed them aside. He searched their bags and found silver coins in every one. The brothers were speechless with confusion. Inside Benjamin's sack, the steward found the missing cup. Benjamin looked at his brothers, suddenly very afraid. The steward ordered his men to take the brothers back to the governor.

When the sons returned to the governor, they pleaded their innocence and said they had promised their father not to return to Canaan without Benjamin. When the governor was convinced that his brothers would not abandon a second brother, the way they had abandoned him, he revealed his true identity. He then asked the Pharaoh to allow his family to move from Canaan to Egypt.

Father and son were finally re-united but did Jacob continue to punish his brothers or did he forgive them?

SOLUTION

Jacob did neither; it was Joseph, not Jacob, who was given an amazing multi-coloured robe by his father then was left by his brothers in the well.

A GLASS
OF SHERRY

A GLASS OF SHERRY

Sarah Hodgkin got out of the bath and put on her new dress. She plaited her hair and tied it with a new blue ribbon. She went into her bedroom and clicked her suitcase shut and carried it downstairs. Today was a special day because Sarah was going to London to visit her godmother whom she had never met before.

Before Sarah got onto the bus that would take her to the station, her mother said, "Now Beryl's been very good to you over the years so I want you to show your appreciation and be on your best behaviour."

"Yes, mother," Sarah said, wriggling free of her mother's embrace.

"Oh, stop fidgeting, dear. You'll be just fine. Here's some money for a taxi to Beryl's house. She's expecting you for supper at six o'clock, so I want you to go straight there and, for heaven's sake, don't talk to strangers."

When Sarah got to the station, she pulled out her train schedule. The next train was leaving at four-fifteen. Sarah checked her watch. It was twelve minutes past four. She didn't know which platform to go to and there was a long queue at the ticket booth. She ran down one set of stairs to platforms 1 and 2. The tracks were empty. She looked as far as she could see in one direction, then the other. Suddenly she heard a whistle blow and looked across at platforms 3 and 4. The train to London was slowly pulling out.

Sarah sighed and lugged her suitcase up the stairs and down again on the other side. She checked the board for the next train which was in half an hour. She sat down on a bench and pulled the end of her plait into her mouth and sat nervously chewing her hair and waiting.

When at last she was on a train and speeding towards London, Sarah felt very grown-up for her age. She didn't know any girls from her village who had ever taken the train to London all by themselves. She felt so excited that she stopped worrying about the fact that she had missed the four-fifteen train and was going to be late for supper - after all, one had to make allowances for world travellers such as herself. She gazed at her reflection in the window, then quickly whisked the ribbon out of her hair and crumpled it into her pocket. She was too old for such girlish things.

It was six-thirty when the taxi pulled up in front of Beryl's house. Sarah paid the driver and walked up the path and rang the doorbell. A few seconds later, a plump matronly woman in a frilly pinafore, with a pink face and white hair, opened the door.

"Sarah, sweetheart, I thought you'd never make it," the old woman said. "Come in. Come in and give your godmother a kiss."

Beryl held Sarah's face in her warm, dry hands and nodded approvingly. The smell of roast beef and gravy came wafting down the hall.

"Sorry I'm late," Sarah said.

"Not at all. Supper's not ready yet, so you have a chance to meet the other guests before we eat."

Beryl led Sarah down the hall and showed her the way into the living room. "Peter will get you a glass of sherry, won't you Peter?" she said, still holding Sarah by the hand. "We're celebrating today. Oh dear, I keep forgetting. You're only thirteen. Don't tell your mother that I've been giving you sherry, mind you. But just this once."

Beryl gave Sarah's hand a quick squeeze, then disappeared back into the kitchen leaving her guests to make their own introductions.

Peter came over and took Sarah's coat, then went over to the sideboard and poured her a generous amount of sherry. "I'm Peter," he said, "if you haven't already figured that out. And this is my brother, John."

John stood up and crossed the room and shook Sarah's hand. "Pleasure to meet you," he said, then sat down again.

"This is Diana," Peter continued, "and this is Rachel."

The two women did not stand up but smiled and nodded. Sarah took a sip of sherry and made a face.

"Ever had sherry before?" Peter asked.

"No," she answered feeling the warmth spread out from her stomach. "It's nice, though."

"In small amounts," John said in a paternal sort of way.

"Oh, lighten up," Rachel said nudging him gently. "It's a special occasion."

"What are you celebrating?" Sarah asked.

"Our anniversaries," Diana said. "Mine and John's."

"Oh," Sarah said, still standing in the middle of the room, unsure of what to say.

"Why don't you have a seat?" Peter asked.

Sarah looked around the living-room. John and Rachel were seated on the sofa to her left. Peter and Diana were sitting on the sofa to her right. There didn't seem to be any extra room on either, but there wasn't another chair to sit on.

"Move over, John' Peter said, "and make room for..."

"Sarah," she said.

"For Sarah. You don't mind, do you, John?"

"Well," John said, "considering I married Rachel two years ago, I guess I don't mind sitting close to her. But the same could be said for you, Peter. You see," John explained to Sarah, "Peter married Diana three years ago. Has it been three years, Diana?"

"Yes, three years," Diana said. "Time flies, doesn't it?"

"But I thought you said you and John were celebrating your anniversary?" Sarah said.

"That's right," Diana said.

"So then you two must be divorced," Sarah said addressing John and Diana.

"No, dear. Never divorced or remarried." Diana said with a wry smile as if she knew something Sarah didn't.

Sarah started to feel uncomfortable. Maybe the sherry had gone to her head. Maybe she had been rude to ask such a direct question. She couldn't figure out who was married to who. The only thing she could be certain of was that John and Peter were brothers. Or were they? Sarah felt like crying. She wished her mother was there to help her. She wanted to talk to Beryl. Suddenly she didn't feel so grown-up anymore.

Sarah waited a while longer and tried to smile politely as the four guests continued to talk and laugh amongst themselves. She waited for a lull in the conversation, then quickly excused herself and ran into the kitchen with tears welling up in her eyes. When Beryl saw her, she opened her arms wide saying, "Come, come, what's the matter dear?"

After Sarah was finally able to explain what all her confusion was about, her godmother easily set her straight. How?

71

SOLUTION

Her godmother told her that both John and Peter were clergymen.

John had married Rachel to another man two years ago and Peter had married Diana to another man three years ago.

John and Diana were not married; they simply shared the same birthday, which everyone was celebrating the night Sarah went to dinner with her godmother

OVERDRIVE

OVERDRIVE

I wanna tell you about the most incredible car wreck I've ever seen. So what, you say, we've all seen 'em, and none of 'em are pretty. Well, the first thing that I have to tell you is that I have seen many car wrecks. Many, many car wrecks. Big deal, you're thinking. Another rubber-necker. Another "slow-down-I-wanna-see-if-anyone-died" creep. Let me explain. You see, I work for the state's Auto Accident Investigation Bureau. Wrecks are my business. I wouldn't say that I've seen more traffic accidents than you've had hot dinners, on account of how I don't know how partial you are to a sandwich, but let's just say I know what I'm talking about.

But this one was different. One of them car racing commentators would probably say something like "the car left the road like a bullet from a gun', which is fine and dandy, and exactly the sort of thing that he is paid to say, but not, in my opinion, wholly accurate. Not really. You see, a number of people saw this incident, and they probably wouldn't say "the car left the road like a bullet from a gun". No sir. What these people would probably say, is that "the car left the road like a ton of over-powered and over-priced steel in the hands of someone who didn't have the first idea how to drive it in a way that didn't endanger either his own self, his passengers, or other road users." That, you could say, is witnesses for you, but hell, they do have a point.

For starters, the car, all $26,599 of it, was an instant write-off. OK, so the insurance company pays for all that. At least, they probably will. The one thing that they can't quibble about is the value of the car. That's to say, up until the accident, the car didn't have much chance to devalue itself, having only been out of the car lot for three hours. Nothing should go wrong with any car within three hours of purchase. Bad luck, huh? Just wait. It gets worse.

The car was a DG4 Turbo, which is a lotta horsepower, particularly for a 21st birthday present. Now I can hear you getting all steamed up, and with good reason too. Two good reasons, in fact. The first is that, yes, it does seem kinda dumb to give a 21-year-old kid a car capable of that sorta power. OK, so every 21-year-old reading this is bleating on that they are considered adults by every federal law and how can I be so patronising blah-blah-blah. Well, stow it, and stow it good. I wouldn't give no 21-year-old of mine a car like that, like I wouldn't give them a 12-gauge shotgun. On top of that, I don't think I'm treading on many toes when I say $26,599 is a big chunk of change to spend on anyone's birthday.

Now this leads us to the weirdness of this wreck. Let's

name names. The 21-year-old in question was Trent Brookner. Doesn't ring any bells? That doesn't surprise me. Trent Brookner was an unexceptional college student, never the smartest monkey in the tree, nor would he ever be. But if I tell you his full name was Trent Leonard Brookner III, maybe that changes things? No? OK, remember how I said the car was a gift? Well, the name on the cheque was Lenny Brookner. As in Little Lenny Brookner? Still nothing? Jesus, some people! Well, Little Lenny was a singing star, back in the 50s. I guess you'd call him a rock 'n' roller, but he was country deep down inside. Anyhow, he had a couple of hits, "Prissy Little Miss' and the like, then went back to country. Made himself a barrelful of money, and bought some land here in town. Started to make more money from real estate than from singing, so he took it up full-time. Come the end of the 80s, he was a big man in town. Next step up was mayor, which Lenny accepted with open arms.

I can see you're looking at me thinking, why is this galoot telling me the life story of someone I've never met. Well, as I said, Lenny bought his boy this hot rod, but as you can guess, he never got to see him drive it. I mean it looks like he never saw him drive it until the very last minute, and then he saw him up real close. Trent loses control of his new toy, just as his daddy is coming round the blind corner on Oakland Drive. The DG4 hits the crash barrier, and slaps Daddy's Caddy into a tree. Now Lenny, he walks away. OK, so both his arms are broke, but he gets clear, which is lucky, 'cause his Caddy goes up in smoke.

Trent, on the other hand, ain't so lucky. Hell, getting arms broke by your idiot son in some fancy car you've just given to him for 26 big ones ain't lucky at all, but Brookner Junior is a mess. The paramedics spend three hours getting him out of the car, and then it's touch and go all the way to the ER at County General.

Trent has lost a lot of blood, and he's been out for the count, but the medics reckon if they can get him to the hospital, then he stands a fighting chance. So when he's still breathing as they roll him into the ER, everyone feels kinda like they're winning. They take him into the theatre, and everyone's scrubbed down, and they're all fighting for him, the whole bit. Then, and this is the really weird part, the surgeon comes in, takes one look at him and says "Find another surgeon. I can't operate on this boy, he's my son."

Since we know that Trent's father was also involved in the car crash, how could he be about to operate on his son?

77

SOLUTION

He wasn't. The surgeon was the boy's mother.

LINE OF
DESTINY

LINE OF DESTINY

England! Luke Sutzmann could barely keep the stupid grin from his face. He and Suzie had been planning and looking forward to this trip all year - and now, at last they were here. The plane from Baltimore had touched down only a couple of hours ago, and already they had seen their first London policeman, not to mention a whole host of the famous London black cabs.

And now, here they were in the concourse of London's Euston Station, people of all nationalities jostling around them. Luke stared up at the big destination boards, savouring the place-names. Some - such as Birmingham, Manchester and Glasgow - he had heard of; others - like Nuneaton, Tamworth and Milton Keynes - were unfamiliar but nevertheless epitomised the England of his dreams.

But, of course, there was one place above all others that had occupied their thoughts over the last few months: Liverpool! Home of the greatest pop group the world had ever known - John, Paul, Ringo and George - otherwise known as The Beatles! In just a few hours they would be arriving at the city's top hotel, The Adelphi, for the annual Beatles Fan Club Convention.

The destination boards rolled. Suzie nudged him. "Look. Platform Twelve." Under the column headed '12', the magic words 'Liverpool Lime Street' had appeared. Luke and Suzie grinned at each other. They picked up their cases, and headed towards the gate for Platform Twelve.

At Liverpool Lime Street, John Hargreaves and his wife, Sarah, waited on Platform Five for the London train. Sarah was fumbling in her handbag. John looked down fondly at her.

"Lost something?"

"Oh, no. Just checking I remembered the map." She smiled and showed him a postcard-sized map of the London Underground.

John smiled. After twenty-five years, he was still as charmed as ever by Sarah's thoughtfulness.

"We won't be needing that," he said. "We'll get a taxi from Euston."

Sarah looked up at him doubtfully. "Won't that be expensive?"

John grinned. "I've told you already. This is our anniversary. For once, we're going first-class all the way!" Looking over Sarah's head, he saw a train pulling in to the platform. "Here it is, and dead on time."

Luke and Suzie walked along the platform to a carriage near the front of the train. They sat either side of a small table, arranging their baggage as best they could. Luke opened his rucksack and took out the well-thumbed convention programme. He flicked through it, then looked up at his girlfriend.

"When we've checked in, maybe we could have a walk round - see a few of the sights?"

Suzie raised her eyebrows. "After a three-hour train

journey? I'm not going anywhere till I've had a shower and changed. Then there'll just be time for a meal before the opening session. You don't want to miss that, do you?"

"Course not." Luke grinned. "You're right, Suze. There'll be plenty of time for sightseeing tomorrow."

Suzie smiled. "Sure. We've gotta do the city tour, right? The Cavern Club, Penny Lane, Strawberry Fields..." They both joined in with the refrain: "Strawberry fields for ever..."

There was a gentle jolt, and the train began to move. It travelled slowly at first, then began to accelerate... taking them the first few miles down the track towards their Merseyside Mecca.

John led Sarah down the platform and opened the door to the first-class carriage. He helped her up the step, then followed with the cases. They had just settled into their seats when the train began to move.

John smiled contentedly. The first-class tickets had been double the usual price, but he had no doubt that the luxury was worth the expense on this occasion.

Opposite him, Sarah leant forward. "Are you going to let me in on where we're going, then?"

"Thought I'd keep that a secret a while longer. You might not like it, and want to get off and go home."

"There's no chance of that, is there?" She tapped his ankle - playfully, but hard enough to indicate that she was serious. "Come on, man of mystery. Spill the beans!"

"OK, then." He took a deep breath. "What's the most .

famous London hotel?"

Sarah gazed at him. "The Hilton?"

"Guess again."

"Not...The Dorchester?"

"Exactly." He grinned.

"But how on earth can...?"

"Well," John began, "I've had a bit of good luck..."

Gradually, the urban landscape outside the carriage windows changed to fields and open countryside. The train was going at high speed now. As they flew through another station, Luke just managed to read a sign saying 'Watford Junction'.

Suzie had fallen silent; her eyes were closed. For a while, Luke pored over the convention programme, trying once again to decide whether they should go to the Bootleg Beatles concert, or attend the talk with former Beatles producer George Martin. On this occasion, The Bootleg Beatles won.

He sat back and started to doze but was woken by voices from the seats behind. He listened idly. There were two men, talking in what Luke thought he recognised as Cockney accents. He quickly gathered that they were off-duty railwaymen.

"Makin' good time, ain't he? Sid must be on a promise tonight!"

His companion laughed. "We get to Kilsby Tunnel in a bit

83

He'll have to slow down there."

"Kilsby," the first man said. "That's half way to Liverpool, in fact it's just before Rugby, ain't it? You know it's single track through there at the moment?"

"Oh. Why's that then?"

"Vandals." The man made it sound like a swear-word. "They dug up the track, and it's still bein' repaired. Just as well someone noticed before a train went through, or there'd have been a Godalmighty disaster..."

Sarah's first reaction to finding out they were staying at The Dorchester had been one of shock at the cost but when John told her about his larger-than-expected annual bonus from Whiteley's, her normal joie de vivre returned. John showed her the brochure the hotel had sent, and they stared wonderingly at the pictures of the piano lounge, the cocktail bar, and the enormous velvet-draped bedrooms. Soon they were laughing like teenagers who had outwitted their parents and were heading off for a naughty weekend.

The sound of the train changed slightly. Looking outside, John was just in time to see Tamworth station rushing past. Suddenly the PA system crackled to life. "Next stop, Rugby. Change at Rugby for Northampton and Coventry. Next stop, Rugby."

The two railwaymen fell silent again. Luke touched Suzie's foot with his own. She glanced up.

"I thought you were asleep," Luke said.

'Not really." Suzie smiled. "How much further do we have to go?"

"Another hour and a half. Do you want a drink from the buffet car?"

"Yeah, great. Can you get me a coffee?"

"Sure."

As Luke stood up, the train lurched slightly. Through the window, he saw, as though it had been imprinted on his brain, a sign: Kilsby Tunnel. A moment later, the speeding train plunged from daylight into darkness.

The train pulled slowly out of Rugby station. John stared out of the window. In 90 minutes they would be in London, and not long after that they'd be living the life of luxury - for three days, at any rate - in one of London's top hotels. He leaned forward, willing the train to go faster.

They gathered speed. Outside, John could see trees, fields, a few scattered houses. Then, ahead, he saw the entrance to a tunnel. On a sign above the arch, he was just able to make out one word: KILSBY.

His ears popped as the pressure in the carriage changed. The view of fields and houses changed abruptly to one of dark bricks and snaking cables. And the train screamed onwards - deeper and deeper into Kilsby Tunnel...

Neither train driver applied the brakes, and neither diverted to another line; yet there was no collision. Why?

SOLUTION

Although both trains were travelling along the same line (one going from London to Liverpool; the other going from Liverpool to London), they were travelling at different times of the day.

HIJACK

HIJACK

Johnny Delgardo flicked through the in-flight magazine yet again, but his eyes barely registered the images of exotic locations. His heart was pounding, and his armpits were clammy with sweat. Just as well there was no one with sensitive nostrils sitting next to him, he thought humourlessly.

On the TV above his head, the film had ended and was replaced by a map on which the plane's position was represented by a winking dot. This in turn was replaced by a new display telling him the outside temperature was minus 67 degrees, and the time to destination - New York's La Guardia Airport - 58 minutes. He bit his lip. Soon, very soon, he would have to make his move.

Johnny stood up and opened the locker. He removed the holdall and put it down on the empty seat next to him. He glanced around, but the stewardesses were at the far end of the cabin, and none of the other passengers were watching him with suspicion. So far everything had gone like clockwork. Satisfied, he allowed himself a moment to reflect on his scheme for smuggling the revolver on board.

The plan had been simple but brilliant. He had packed the gun in his holdall, which he carried as hand luggage. He had placed the holdall onto the belt which led into the X-ray machine, and immediately picked an argument with a dumb-looking bald guy who was standing next to him.

'Hey! Watch what you're doing with that trolley, slaphead!

The bald guy looked round, obviously wondering what it was he was supposed to have done. Seeing Johnny's heavy musculature - the result of many hours pumping iron in the prison gym - he decided to temporise. "Sorry, pal. I didn't see you."

'You will be sorry - when I've rearranged your face." Johnny raised his fist and took a step forward. The guy stepped back in a reflex movement, sending a small child behind him sprawling.

'Hey! Mind my kid!" a woman shrieked, as the child began to wail.

A security guard ambled over. "What's going on?"

'This guy tried to flatten my kid..."

'It wasn't my fault. This punk wanted to pick a... Say, where's he gone?"

But Johnny had already collected his holdall and strolled on to the departure lounge. As he hoped, the bored clerk operating the X-ray machine had been distracted by the fracas. As he watched he failed to notice the outline of the revolver as it sailed by on his monitor screen.

The plane shuddered slightly, jolting Johnny back to the present. The in-flight display informed him that there were forty-six minutes to arrival. He couldn't wait any longer. He rummaged inside the holdall until his fingers closed round the cold metal. There was the faintest click as he released the safety catch. Keeping one hand on the revolver, still in the bag, he reached upwards with his other hand and pressed the call button. After a few moments, a young blonde stewardess made her way down the cabin.

'Yes, sir?" She gave him a neutral, professional smile.

Johnny grinned back. "What's your name, baby?"

'Barbara, sir. Was there something, only I'm..."

Johnny locked eyes with her. He leaned forward and lowered his voice to a soft growl. "Listen, Barbara. Inside this bag, I'm holding a US Army revolver. It's pointed right at your pretty face. If you shout or do anything silly, I'll pull the trigger, and you'll never turn any guy's head ever again." He allowed the top of the bag to gape open, so she could see the barrel of the revolver pointing straight at her.

'Oh, no, please..."

'It's OK," Johnny said. "No one's gonna get hurt if you do as I say. Now, take me to the flight deck. I need to speak to the captain."

Barbara led Johnny through the cabin. She stayed cool, but her smile had a distinctly lopsided look now. Johnny kept the gun in the holdall, which he held close to his chest. A plane full of panicking passengers was a complication he didn't want right now.

As they entered the flight deck, the uniformed navigator looked up. "Hi, Barbara. How's my favourite stewardess?" He saw Johnny. "Uh, is there a problem?"

'No problem," Johnny said, grinning. He took the revolver out and pointed it at the navigator's head. "No problem at all."

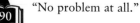

'Aw, heck.' The navigator's jaw dropped. 'A hijack.'

'Got it in one,' Johnny said. 'Do as I say and no one gets hurt. Who's in charge here?'

At the front of the flight deck, a grey-haired man turned round. 'I am. I'm Captain McKenzie. For God's sake, be careful with that gun. What is it you want?'

Johnny's grin widened still further. 'Well, Captain McKenzie, I want you to pass on a message to the people at the control tower down there. Tell them there's a hijacker on board, but there's no need for anyone to panic. We land as normal, but no one leaves the plane till I'm brought three things.'

'And what might they be?'

'A suitcase containing a million bucks in used, unmarked notes, and two parachutes.'

'*Two* parachutes?'

Johnny nodded. 'One for me and one for someone else - I want Judge Leo Underhill brought on board.'

'And then you'll release everyone?'

'Sure. Except for the judge and you, Captain. We're going on another little journey.'

Captain McKenzie stared hard at Johnny, who returned his gaze. 'So who are the parachutes for?' he asked after a couple of seconds.

Johnny pointed the gun at the captain's head. 'Enough talk. Just call the tower, will you?'

Johnny stayed on the flight deck while the crew brought the plane down. As the engines died, Captain McKenzie turned to face him again.

"What do I tell the passengers?" he asked.

Johnny shrugged. "Tell them there's a technical problem. They won't have long to wait."

"How do you know?"

"'Cause you'll explain to the tower that unless I get what I want within an hour, I'll blow your head off."

Fifty-eight minutes after the plane landed, Johnny's demands were met. Two parachutes were delivered, and Judge Leo Underhill himself brought the suitcase containing the cash. Johnny made him drag it all the way to the flight deck. Once he was in there, Johnny allowed the passengers and other crew members to disembark.

It was five and a half years since they had last met in a New York court room, but Leo Underhill had changed little. Judge Underhill was the man who had sent Johnny down for a maximum five-year sentence for what had been little more than a barrack room misunderstanding. Now, though, the boot was on the other foot. Johnny grinned.

"Good to see you again, Judge."

"You won't get away with this, Johnny." Underhill was perspiring heavily, not just from the effort of carrying the heavy suitcase. "Hand over the gun, and we can..."

"Shut up!" Johnny gestured with the revolver. "You're not in court now. Sit there and don't say anything, or I may do something we'll both regret." He turned to the captain. "OK, get us airborne."

"Where are we going? You haven't said..."

"Just head west, and don't look round. Same goes for you, Judge."

The plane took off. Standing behind the judge and Captain McKenzie, Johnny quickly donned a parachute. He had to put down the gun to do so, but he kept it close in case either of them tried to jump him. Clearly, though, neither man had any wish to be a hero. In a few minutes the parachute was in place.

"OK," Johnny said. "Where are we now?"

"Pennsylvania. The outskirts of Pittsburgh."

"Perfect. So long then, gentlemen."

Johnny backed out of the cabin, gun in one hand, suitcase in the other. He opened the front exit door and tumbled backwards. After freefalling for a few seconds, he dropped the gun and pulled the ripcord. A minute or so later, he was gliding softly towards the ground.

Meanwhile, in the aircraft, Captain McKenzie and the judge stared at each other, and at the unused parachute on the flight deck floor. "Well," Captain McKenzie said a little awkwardly, "I guess we'd better head back to La Guardia."

Why did Johnny request two parachutes since he ended up using just one? Had something gone wrong with his plan?

SOLUTION

Nothing went wrong with his plan at all - quite the opposite. The hijacker knew that if he asked for only one parachute, the authorities could easily sabotage it. He therefore asked for Judge Underhill and an extra parachute so that they would think he planned to make the judge jump with him. He knew that then they wouldn't risk tampering with either of the parachutes.